The Bed Book

by Harriet Ziefert
Illustrated by Loek Koopmans

SCHOLASTIC INC.
New York Toronto London Auckland Sydney

off the bed

messy bed

neat bed

under the bed

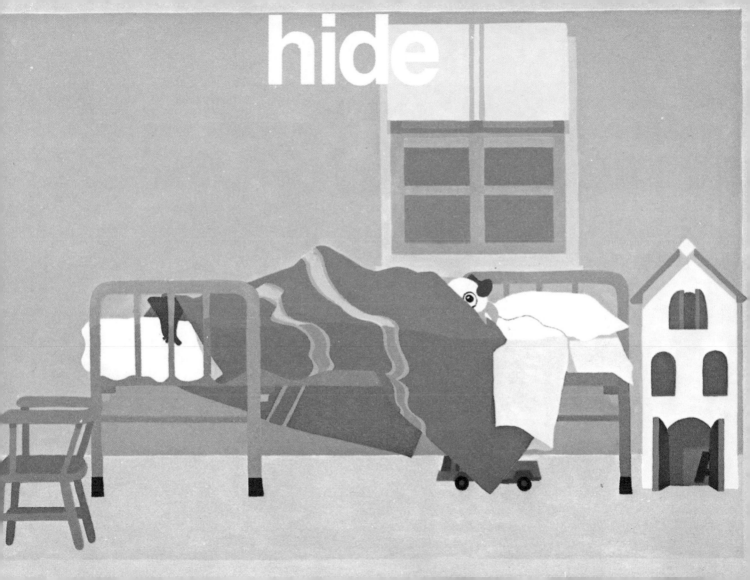

sick bed

jump on the bed

bed at night

I'm going to bed.

Good night!

ISBN 0-590-45261-4

12 11 10 9 8 7 6 5 4   11   4 5 6/9

Printed in the U.S.A.   08